THE GREAT ADVENTURER

SHANE HITCHCOCK

To see more of Shane's work go to: www.shanehitchcock.ca
Or follow him on instagram at: _shanehitchcock_

ISBN 978-0-9936758-1-2

In the tattooed trees
Found deep in the park,
Grows a tree with two names
Carved into its bark.
In the tattooed trees
Found deep in the park,
Our friendship is etched
Inside of a heart.

With love,

Hello

Hello all you earthworms and aliens,
Old folks and children,
Boys and girls,
Rabbits and turtles.
Welcome, welcome to my fort.
Now climb on up,
Step inside
And get ready, my friends,
For a bumpy ride.

Dreams

A dream is a wish, a hope, a prayer,
Until you start to chase it.
Then it turns into a journey
With a destination.

A destination no one knows
Exactly how to find,
'Cause dreams are hidden deep within us,
Fading with the time.

So now's the day,
You mustn't wait,
It's time to start your voyage.
Just pack up a lunch, grab a grin
And muster up some courage.

You'll fight off your naysayers, fears and doubts,
And walk through the darkest of darkness.
And maybe someday you'll meet your dream,
Just follow your dream-finding compass.

Pilot School

There's a gorilla in my locker,
And I don't know what to do.
He's eaten half my pencils,
And he's swallowed all my glue.

There's a gorilla in my locker,
And I'm really getting worried.
My binder's buried deep inside,
And I am in a hurry.

There's a gorilla in my locker,
And I need to get to class.
Today's the most important day,
We're learning how not to crash.

There's a gorilla in my locker,
And it's kind of problematic . . .
Today's a day I mustn't miss,
That's why I'm in a panic.

There's a . . . Oh wait,
Never mind.
It's just my pilot jacket.

Plane Crash

With the wind in my hair and my wings in the air,
I was flying through the Rockies.
Watching the sunset, listening to the snow melt,
Then I felt it,
A jerk and a wiggle.
Then I heard it,
A groan and a grumble.
And before I could think,
I felt a bang and I heard a clink.
I veered to the left, I banked to the right.
I pulled on the throttle with all of my might.

I spun, I flipped, I rose,
I crossed my fingers and crossed my toes.
I dipped, I jittered, I dove,
I zigged, I zagged, my wings tore off.
I caught on fire, my propeller stopped.

I said my prayers and closed my eyes,
I gave the throttle one last try,
But I scraped the trees,
The plane went *bash*.
My teeth knocked out,
My elbow scratched,
I hit the ground
With the sound
Of a four-ton bomb.

Then I opened my eyes,
And to my surprise
Everything was calm.
I'd survived.

Maybe Tomorrow

So the stars didn't align, well that's fine,
Maybe tomorrow they'll be in their place.
But the sun's still gonna shine, and that's why,
I've got a smile that sits on my face.

'Cause the hands on the clock will keep ticking
And nights will turn to days
And sooner or later
The bad'll get better
And things'll start going my way.

It might be tomorrow
Or maybe on Tuesday
Perhaps on Wednesday the eighth.
All I need is some time
And this smile of mine
For the stars to fall back in their place.

'Cause the world's still turning
And it's hard but I'm learning
That everything precious
Takes time.
And it's the days in between
All the good days that seem
To determine if the stars will align.

So the stars didn't align, well that's fine,
Maybe tomorrow they'll be in their place.
But the sun's still gonna shine, and that's why,
I've got a smile that sits on my face.

Yeti Spit

Dribble dribble dribble drip,
I'm standing under a yeti's lip.
Now I don't mind his breath
Or his jokes or his cat,
Because he's the nicest of fellas.
But I do wish this leaking
Yeti would lend me
One of his extra umbrellas.

Hide-and-Seek Pete

My neck sticks out to the side.
It ain't no good when I hide.
I'll stand by a tree
But you'll always find me,
'Cause my neck sticks out to the side.

And my knees are a little bit creaky,
So it's hard for me to be sneaky.
When I crouch down low
You'll know where to go,
'Cause my knees are a little bit creaky.

And my nose it whistles loudly,
So it won't be hard to spot me.
Just wait for a tweet
And my knees to go creak
And my neck to stick out and you'll find me.

So why do they call me hide-and-seek Pete
When I'm no good at hiding?
Well I'll close my eyes
And you go and hide,
And I'll show you how good I'm at finding.

The Dark

The dark is a scary and dangerous place
For a pilot to walk alone,
Surrounded by an endless space,
Within it the unknown.

There are frightening things that lurk in the dark,
Things that have never been seen.
There are things so chilling and horribly haunting,
Those things would make a man scream.

Oh there's so many reasons to stay in the light,
To never go out and explore,
To stay in your cozy candlelit room,
Locked behind your door.

Where you'll never have to face the beasts,
Where you'll never have to fight,
Where you'll never get to conquer your fears,
That lurk in the dark of the night.

Tomato Tornado

A tomato tornado's the messiest kind.
It bends and it winds and it doubles in size,
As it rips the tomatoes straight off the vines,
Up through the air and into the sky.
You'll search for cover, you'll run and you'll hide,
As it spits out tomatoes ten at a time.
They'll splash on your face, you'll get seeds in your eyes,
But don't fight back, trust me I've tried.
The tomato tornado will suck you inside.
It's the stickiest, yuckiest, slimiest ride.
Tomatoes come flying from every side,
And that's why there's no doubt in my mind
The tomato tornado's the messiest kind.

Under the Deep Dark Sea

Under the deep dark sea
Where the mermaids sleep
Lives the most horrendous thing you've ever seen.

Yup that's right,

Way way deep down
Where the fish don't even live
There is a monster so profound
She scares squid.

She uses sharks as toothpicks,
She puts on bright red lipstick
And lures you in with promises of kisses.

And when you get there she doesn't kiss you,
She eats you.
Swallows you up in one big bite,
Bones and everything.
And if you put up a fight
She laughs.

So listen to me,
Listen close to me,
If you're diving deep, deep down in the sea,
Where the fish don't live and the mermaids sleep,
Don't go looking for kisses,
'Cause she's, well, she's looking to eat.

The Tentacle Two-Step

The tentacle two-step is an octopus's nightmare.
With sixteen limbs (eight are his and eight are hers)
It's hard to not get tangled.
So at octopus parties not one of them dances,
Not one of them wiggles or shakes,
Instead they use those limbs they've got
To stuff their mouths with cake.

The Rain

When you're feeling kind of lonely
Thinking no one knows your pain,
Remember this my friend:
An umbrella spends its life
Standing in the rain.

GIB US YAR
GOLD!

Captain Maggie

Captain Maggie McGonigal—
The toughest pirate on the seven seas.
She had a peg for an eye
And a patch on her leg.
Her teeth were steel
But her heart was gold.
So she kept it hidden
But her parrot told.

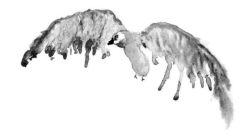

Sunburn

A caterpillar and I
Were napping in the sunshine by the water.

When we got up he'd grown wings,
And I looked like a lobster.

Treasure

Some days you'll follow a map with an *X*
And find a chest of gold.
And some days you'll dig and dig in the sand,
And all you'll find's a hole.
'Cause some days the treasure ain't under the *X*,
Some days the treasure ain't gold.
Some days the treasure's the sun in your eyes
And the story that's yet to be told.

Weird Old Man

I think I asked some pretty good questions
To the weird old man sitting in the tree.
"Why are you up here?
And Why did you climb this giant tree?"
"Well you see," he said to me,
"I didn't climb this giant tree.
I was feeling hungry and needed to eat,
So I found an already-chewed-up apple core
And waited seven years or more.
I sat on the seed through sunlight and storms,
Through cold and warm,
And soon the tree grew under me,
And the branches spread and sprouted leaves,
And flowers bloomed and lured the bees,
And an apple grew, and then there were two,
And soon there were four, and then there were more.
There were apples galore.
And now—
Now I'm up here chompin' and swingin' my feet,
'Cause ain't it just a real treat
To have these juicy apples to eat."

Trap

If you're out to catch some supper
And you've just set up your trap,
Try your best to remember . . .
Exactly where it's at.

Wrong or Right

If everything were black and white
The rainbow would be bland.
If everything were wrong or right
We'd probably understand.

But sometimes things are in between
And could go either way.
Like sometimes wrong things kinda seem
Like right things on the day.

So try your best to do what's right,
But remember that you're human.
And that sometimes even when you try,
You don't know what you're doin'.

Magician

A magician pulled a rabbit out of my hat,
So I asked for it back.
So he gave me my hat,
And I reached in a little deeper,
And pulled out a sailor, his boat and its anchor,
A helicopter, a gator, a doctor,
A lion, a juggler, an opera singer,
A table, a menu, a plate and a waiter,
Who brought me spaghetti, a salad and lobster.
Then out popped a cop who was chasing a robber
With coins in her hands—
He grabbed her and cuffed her.
If that ain't enough, the story gets weirder.

A ship with an alien armed with a laser
Fell out of my hat and abducted the robber,
The cop and the waiter, my fabulous dinner,
The juggler, the lion, the opera singer,
The helicopter, the doctor,
The sailer, his boat and its anchor,
The rabbit and also the gator.
And the shocked magician, he clapped and he cheered,
So I put on my hat and I disappeared.

Crocodile Crosswalk

This crocodile crosswalk
I never should have crossed,
It's breathing on my feet
And it's opening up its jaws.

I would have taken the bridge,
But its ropes were worn and frayed,
From ugly hungry rats
That were noisily nibbling away.

This crocodile crosswalk
It looked like it was safe,
But now I'm halfway 'cross
And it's looking like it ain't.

This crocodile crosswalk
I thought it would be fine,
But just like worn-out ropes
It could SNAP at any time.

Star

I found a bird
And flew away.
We left the earth
For outer space.
I grabbed a star
And claimed it mine.
And named it you
Because you shine.

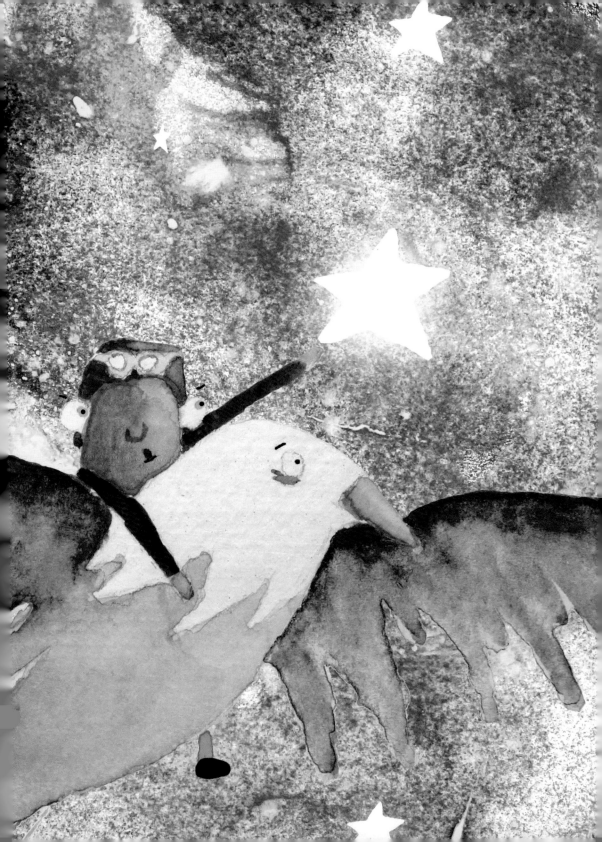

Ugly Elvis

Ugly Elvis was only ugly on the out.
With his heart stuffed full of kindness,
He was beautiful no doubt.
It was only on the inside though,
His beauty ever shone.
He thought this through his final days,
Not knowing he was wrong.

What Elvis didn't realize,
Was that his kindness shone so bright,
He was beautiful on the inside
And the outside every night.

There's a Whale In My Hat

There's a whale in my hat,
And I don't know why he's there.
He's much too large
And much too blue
To ever be my hair.

And there's a cricket in my sock,
Who's doing me no good.
He's much too small
And crickety
To ever be my foot.

And there's a minnow in my glove,
Who doesn't understand,
He's much too young
And slippery
To ever be my hand.

"Now just out of curiosity,
Where is my hair?" I asked.
"It's swimming in the ocean," said the whale,
"That's why I crawled into your hat."

"And I snuck into your sock," said the cricket,
"While your foot was chirping in the grass."

"And what about my hand?" I asked.

"Well," said the minnow,
"He's hanging from a fishing pole.
I tricked him onto that."

Poor Big Monster

"You've certainly got a lot of negativity
Coming out of your mouth."
I said to the monster as he moped.

"I'm just too tall," he said,
"And my teeth are too sharp
And my head,
It's got horns
And I'm ugly and no fun—
People see me and run.

My fur's all matted, I'm hated,
They've chased me out of town and they'll never let me back.
There's no chance.
I'll bet my pants
If I tried to come back
They'd just run at me with their fire sticks
And pitchforks and shake their fists
And yell my name
And chase me back to the forest again.

And maybe that's why all I say is sad
And all I do is mope
And all I've got is hurt
'Cause what I've lost is hope."

Oh that poor big monster, I thought to myself,
He's just as fragile as everyone else.

You see I learnt that day as I walked away,
That even the biggest and toughest of guys
Can be caught sometimes
With tears in their eyes.

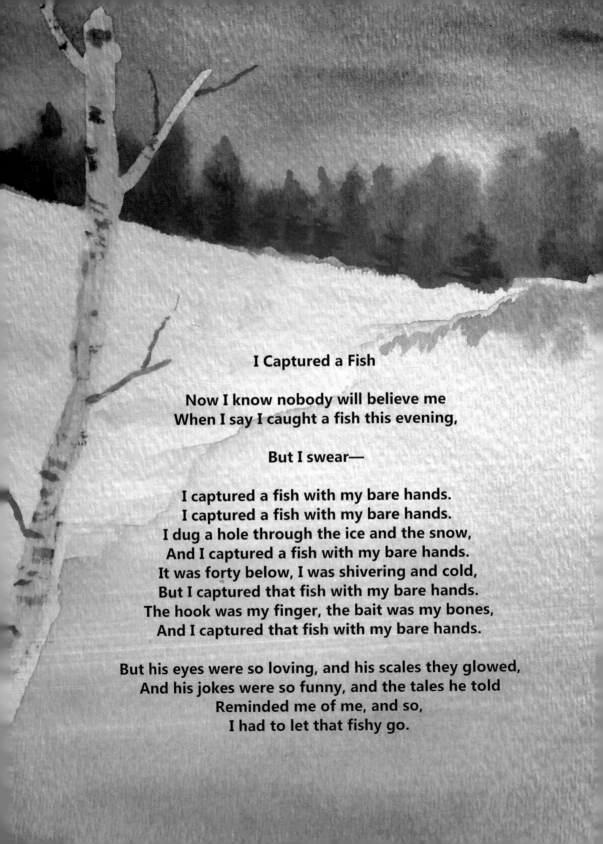

I Captured a Fish

Now I know nobody will believe me
When I say I caught a fish this evening,

But I swear—

I captured a fish with my bare hands.
I captured a fish with my bare hands.
I dug a hole through the ice and the snow,
And I captured a fish with my bare hands.
It was forty below, I was shivering and cold,
But I captured that fish with my bare hands.
The hook was my finger, the bait was my bones,
And I captured that fish with my bare hands.

But his eyes were so loving, and his scales they glowed,
And his jokes were so funny, and the tales he told
Reminded me of me, and so,
I had to let that fishy go.

Eight Months

It's been eight months without a bath.
No soap, no soak, no suds, no clean.
So plug your noses, run and scream.
I'm a downright nasty stink machine.

I walk around in a cloud of "gross."
Was sniffed by a skunk and he broke his nose.
Flies rent the cracks between my toes.
It's been eight months without a bath.

My breath burns the bark off the backs of trees.
Animals migrate to stay up-breeze.
Even the maggots are allergic to me.
It's been eight months without a bath.

I once saw a dung beetle stop and stare.
There's moss growing out of my underwear . . .
So if anyone's got a loofah to spare?
It's been eight months without a bath.

Balloons

Holding our hearts we flew through the sky,
And soon balloon *U*, it found balloon *I*.
And we got all tangled and drifted together,
Up through the clouds
And into forever.

The Great Adventurer

He's flown in rocket ships
All 'round the moon.
He's fought dragons, seized castles
And built robots in his room.
He's journeyed through the darkest caves,
Fighting bats off, finding gold.
He's climbed the highest mountains
While braving the coldest of cold.
He's skirmished on pirate ships
Across the seven seas,
Drawn swords with their captains
And brought them to their knees.
He stole the *Mona Lisa*
And escaped from sixteen cops.
Oh what a wild life he's lived
Inside that cardboard box.